On Wings of Words

Senior Authors
Albert J. Harris
Mae Knight Clark

THE MACMILLAN READING PROGRAM
Primary Grades

When you read a book
You can be anything!
You can fly on wings of words!
And be a pirate or a king
Or a giant or a witch
Or a lion in the zoo—
Till you close the book
And go back to being you.

"When You Read a Book,"
by Miriam Hershenson

On Wings of Words

Betty H. Yarborough

THE MACMILLAN COMPANY
COLLIER-MACMILLAN LIMITED, LONDON

Copyright © The Macmillan Company 1971

All rights reserved. No part of this book may be reproduced or transmitted in any form or by any means, electronic or mechanical, including photocopying, recording, or by any information storage or retrieval system, without permission in writing from the Publisher.

THE MACMILLAN COMPANY
866 Third Avenue, New York, New York 10022
COLLIER-MACMILLAN CANADA, LTD., TORONTO, ONTARIO
Printed in the United States of America

1-M

ILLUSTRATED BY

Mac Conner, Jack Endewelt, Ethel Gold,
Paul Granger, Les Gray, Ib Ohlsson,
Ralph Pinto, Ted Schroeder

Grateful acknowledgment is made to the following authors
and publishers for permission to use copyrighted material:

Thomas Y. Crowell Company, Inc., for "Weather Is Full of the Nicest Sounds," from *I Like Weather* by Aileen Fisher. Copyright © 1963 by Aileen Fisher.

Doubleday & Company, Inc., for "Elves and Apple Trees," from *Taxis and Toadstools* by Rachel Field. Copyright 1926 by Doubleday & Company, Inc. Reprinted by permission of the publisher. In the British Empire by permission of World's Work Ltd.; for "The Orange Tree," adapted from *For Pepita—An Orange Tree* by Claire Oleson. Copyright © 1967 by Doubleday & Company, Inc. Used by permission of the publisher.

E. P. Dutton & Co., Inc., for "Jump or Jiggle" by Evelyn Beyer, from *Another Here and Now Story Book* by Lucy Sprague Mitchell. Copyright, 1937, by E. P. Dutton & Co., Inc. Renewal, ©, 1967 by Lucy Sprague Mitchell. Reprinted by permission of the publishers.

Golden Press, Inc., for "A Pickle for a Nickel," reprinted and adapted by permission from *A Pickle for a Nickel* by Lilian Moore. Copyright © 1961 by Golden Press, Inc.; for "The Saggy Baggy Elephant," reprinted and adapted by permission from *The Saggy Baggy Elephant* by Kathryn and Byron Jackson. Copyright © 1947 by Golden Press, Inc.

Miss Miriam Hershenson, for "When You Read a Book" by Miriam Hershenson.

J. B. Lippincott Company, for "Ring Around the World," from *All Through the Year* by Annette Wynne. Copyright 1932, 1960 by Annette Wynne. Published by J. B. Lippincott Company.

William Morrow and Company, Inc., for "Louis Makes a Friend," adapted from *Bayou Boy* by Eleanor Frances Lattimore, copyright © 1946 by William Morrow and Company, Inc., reprinted by permission of the publisher.

Charles Scribner's Sons, for "A Cricket," reprinted with the permission of Charles Scribner's Sons from *Cricket in a Thicket* by Aileen Fisher. Copyright © 1963 Aileen Fisher; for "Sky Net," reprinted with the permission of Charles Scribner's Sons from *In the Woods, In the Meadow, In the Sky* by Aileen Fisher. Copyright © 1965 Aileen Fisher.

Albert Whitman & Company, for "Tommy-On-Time," adapted from *Tommy-On-Time* by Virginia Novinger. Copyright 1952 by Albert Whitman & Company. Reprinted by permission of the publisher.

Contents

Tommy-On-Time 9
    VIRGINIA NOVINGER

A Pickle for a Nickel 19
    LILIAN MOORE

The Sad Princess 28
    FOLK TALE

Joe 38
    BETTY H. YARBOROUGH

Weather Is Full of the Nicest Sounds *(Poem)* 46
    AILEEN FISHER

Gus 48
    BETTY H. YARBOROUGH

River, River 56
    BETTY H. YARBOROUGH

Louis Makes A New Friend 61
    ELEANOR FRANCES LATTIMORE

Ring Around the World *(Poem)* 68
    ANNETTE WYNNE

Crick-Crick 69
    BETTY H. YARBOROUGH

A Cricket *(Poem)* 78
    AILEEN FISHER

The Shoemaker and the Elves 79
    GRIMM FAIRY TALES
Elves and Apple Trees *(Poem)* 88
    RACHEL FIELD
Peter's Trip to the Bay 89
    BETTY H. YARBOROUGH
Peter and the Frogmen 96
Truck-Riding Hen 108
    BETTY H. YARBOROUGH
Rosa 116
    BETTY H. YARBOROUGH
The Black Puppy 124
Jump or Jiggle *(Poem)* 130
    EVELYN BEYER
The Saggy Baggy Elephant 131
    KATHRYN and BYRON JACKSON
The Orange Tree 139
    CLAIRE OLESON
Birthday Packages 146
Sky Net *(Poem)* 156
    AILEEN FISHER

Tommy-On-Time

Tommy walked to school each day. He walked home, too. Many days Tommy didn't get to school on time. Many days he didn't get home on time.

One day his mother said, "Tommy, you are late for lunch again."

Tommy said, "I saw a man painting a little doghouse. I had to stop to see what he was doing."

After lunch Tommy didn't get back to school on time. No one was there but Miss White.

9

Miss White said, "You are late again, Tommy. Your friends are at the school play."

"May I go, too?" asked Tommy.

"No, you can't go now," Miss White said. "You are too late. You are Tommy-Too-Late again."

The next day Tommy got to school on time. He got home for lunch on time. After lunch he got back to school on time, too.

As Tommy walked home after school, he saw a big truck. He had to stop and look at it. It was not like the trucks Tommy had seen before. It had a house on it. The truck was going very slowly down the street.

A man was looking at the truck.
"Why is the truck going so slowly?"
Tommy asked the man.

"It has a house on it," the man said.

"Where is the truck taking the house?"
Tommy asked.

"The truck is taking the house
to the next street," the man said.

"Why is the truck taking the house
to the next street?" asked Tommy.

"The people who live in it
want to take it there," the man said.

"Why don't they get a new house?"
Tommy asked.

"They like this house," said the man.
Then the truck had to stop.

"Why did the truck stop?"
asked Tommy.

"Do you see the tree?
The truck can't take the house
by the tree," said the man.

"How will the truck get the house
by the tree?" asked Tommy.

"The men in the truck will cut
the tree," said the man.

"I want to see them do it,"
said Tommy.

It was late, but Tommy didn't care.
It was fun to see the truck
with the house on it.

The men cut the tree. The truck
went slowly down the street.
Then Tommy went home.

Tommy's mother said, "Where were
you, Tommy? You are very late."

"I saw a big truck," said Tommy.
"It had a house on it. It was taking
the house to the next street. I had to stop
and look at it. A man told me
all about it. I had fun."

"But, Tommy, Daddy was looking
for you. He went fishing in the new boat.

He wanted to take you with him," his mother said.

"Can't I go now?" asked Tommy.

"No, Tommy. You are too late," said his mother.

Tommy was very sad. He was too late to go fishing with his daddy.

"Tommy, if you don't like to be Tommy-Too-Late, why don't you try to be Tommy-On-Time? You can be Tommy-On-Time if you try," his mother said.

"On school days you must not stop to look at things. You must not stop to talk to people. You must hurry to school. You must hurry home, too."

"I can stop to look at things on days we don't have school," said Tommy. "I can stop to talk with people, too."

"Yes," said his mother. "Then you won't be Tommy-Too-Late on school days."

The next morning as Tommy walked to school he saw a little red bird in a tree. But he didn't stop to look at the bird.

"See you later, Red Bird," said Tommy. He had to hurry to school.

Then Tommy saw a policeman he knew. The policeman said, "Hello, Tommy. How are you?"

"All right," said Tommy. "But I have to hurry. I have to get to school on time."

Tommy got to school on time.

Miss White was happy. She said, "Tommy, you are in time to help me put away the books. Do you want to help me?"

"Oh, yes," said Tommy.

Tommy put away the books.

At lunchtime Tommy ran home. Down the street he saw a bus with many people on it. Tommy wanted to know where the bus was taking the people.

Tommy wanted to stop to look at the bus. But he was in a hurry.

When Tommy got home, he asked, "Am I late?"

"No," said his mother. "You are on time."

"I didn't stop to look at things," Tommy said. "I didn't stop to talk."

"Good," said his mother. "I knew you could be on time if you tried."

After school Tommy walked home again. He saw a white rabbit in a cage. He didn't stop to look at it.

He said, "Hello, Rabbit. See you later."

Then he saw a man in a tree. He wanted to ask the man what he was doing. But he didn't stop to ask him. Tommy had to hurry home.

When Tommy got home,
his mother said, "Oh, Tommy, you
are not late. I am so happy.
Daddy is home. He wants
to take you for a ride in the boat."

"That will be fun," said Tommy.
"Where is Daddy?"

"He went out to get the boat ready.
Let's tell him that Tommy-On-Time
is here."

"Yes," said Tommy. "Let's tell him
that I won't ever be Tommy-Too-Late
again. I will be Tommy-On-Time
from now on."

A Pickle for a Nickel

Mr. Peters lived in an old brown house on a quiet little street.

He didn't live there all by himself. He had a bird.

Mr. Peters' bird was named Pedro. Pedro didn't talk, as many birds of his kind do. He was very quiet.

Mr. Peters liked Pedro. He said, "That's my good Pedro."

Mr. Peters was a quiet man. He didn't want noise in his house. Each morning Mr. Peters went off to work. Each night he came back to his quiet house. Mr. Peters was happy.

Down the street there was
a little white house. No one lived in it.
Then one day people came to live
in the little white house.

"I see a father," said Mr. Peters
to himself. "I see a mother.
I see a little boy. Boys make noise.
Boys like **noise**."

Mr. Peters didn't say anything
to the new people. But each morning
Mr. Peters went off to work. So there were
things Mr. Peters didn't know.

He didn't know that the boy's name
was Bill. He didn't know
that Bill had no one to play with him.

He didn't know that Bill came
up the quiet little street to see who lived
in the old brown house.

Mr. Peters didn't know Bill at all.
But Pedro did.

Bill went to see Mr. Peters. He
was not there. Pedro was in his cage
by a window. When Bill saw the bird
at the window, he went up to the screen
to look at him.

"Hello," said Bill. "Do you want
a pickle for a nickel?"

The bird didn't say anything.
He just looked at the boy.

After that, Bill came to see the bird many times. Each day after lunch Bill came to the old brown house and went to the window to see Pedro.

"Hello," said Bill. "Do you want a pickle for a nickel?"

Bill talked and talked to Pedro. He said all kinds of things to him. "Do you want a pickle for a nickel?" asked Bill each day.

Pedro just looked at Bill. He didn't say a word.

Then one night when Mr. Peters came home to his quiet old house there was a noise. A big **noise!**

"Want a pickle for a nickel?"

Mr. Peters jumped. Who was in the house?

There it was again.

"Pickle! Pickle! Pickle! For a nickel!"

Mr. Peters ran into the house.

It was Pedro.

Mr. Peters put something over Pedro's cage. Then Pedro was quiet again.

Mr. Peters couldn't eat. He was very sad. "Oh," said Mr. Peters to himself. "How can I help Pedro?"

In the morning Pedro talked again. "A pickle for a nickel," he said.

After that Mr. Peters didn't know what to do. Pedro was talking all the time.

Then one morning Mr. Peters saw Bill.

"Boys like **noise**!" said Mr. Peters to himself.

Mr. Peters took the cage with Pedro in it. He walked down the street to the little white house. He walked right up to Bill.

"Boy," said Mr. Peters. "Do you want a bird?"

Bill looked at Pedro. He looked at Mr. Peters.

"A bird!" said Bill. "For me?"

"I don't want this bird now," said Mr. Peters. "He talks all the time. He was a very quiet bird. But now he talks and talks. I don't want a talking bird. Do you want him?"

Bill wanted to say, "Oh, yes!
Yes, I do." But he had to ask his mother.
He ran into the house. Then he ran out
again. His mother had said
he could have the bird.

"Well, do you want the bird?"
asked Mr. Peters.

Bill wanted to say, "Yes! Yes! Yes!"
But first he had something to tell
Mr. Peters.

"Mr. Peters," said Bill,
"I didn't know you wanted a quiet bird.
I was the one who got him to talk."

"You!" said Mr. Peters.

He put down Pedro's cage.

"So, you got him to talk? Well,
now you can have him. Good day."

Mr. Peters slowly walked away
from the little white house.

Bill ran to Pedro's cage.

"Oh, Pedro!" he said.
"Now you are my bird."

"Want a pickle for a nickel?" asked Pedro.

At last Mr. Peters' old brown house was quiet again. Mr. Peters was by himself and there was no noise. No noise at all. Mr. Peters was happy again.

But there was noise all the time at the little white house. Pedro and Bill were happy, too

The Sad Princess

There was a time when a princess lived in a big castle.

The princess was very kind. She knew many things. But she was sad all the time. The pretty princess couldn't laugh.

When the princess was a baby, her mother got her pretty things with which to play. The princess played with them. But they didn't make her laugh.

When the princess was a little girl, her father took her to a fair.
She saw many things to make her laugh.
But she didn't laugh at anything she saw.

The princess' mother and father wanted to make her laugh. They tried and tried, but they couldn't.

The princess didn't have many friends. She didn't talk to people. She was quiet all the time.

On holidays all the people had a good time, but the princess didn't. She didn't know how to have fun.

At last it was time for the princess to marry. The princess' father talked to his people. "I want the princess to be happy," he said. "The man who can make her laugh may marry her."

From that day on, men from all around came to the castle to see the pretty princess. They all wanted to marry her.

One man came with pretty birds in a cage. The birds were for the princess. She liked the birds, but she didn't laugh.

One man came up to the castle on a cow. All the people laughed at him, but the princess didn't laugh.

A man came with a dog that did tricks, but the princess didn't laugh.

The next man told a story
to make the princess laugh.
The princess' father laughed and laughed,
but not the princess.

The pretty princess was kind to all
who came to see her. She told each man
that she liked what he did for her.
But she didn't laugh.

Each man wanted to marry
the princess. But the princess didn't want
to marry one of them. She would not have
a man who could not make her laugh.

One day a farm boy heard about the princess. He had little to give her. He didn't know how to do tricks to make her laugh. But he wanted to help the princess.

He said to himself, "I will go to see the princess. I will make her laugh."

The boy went off to find the castle where the princess lived. On the way to the castle, the farm boy saw a little old man.

"I want something to eat," said the little old man. "Will you give me something?"

The farm boy had just one little cake. But he said, "You may have my cake."

When he said that, the little old man went away and the farm boy saw a big golden goose.

"Oh!" laughed the boy. "I will take the golden goose to the princess." So he took the goose and walked on to the castle.

Then he saw three girls. They saw the golden goose. Each girl wanted it. One of them tried to take the goose from the boy. But when she did, she could not let go.

One of the other girls tried
to get the first girl away
from the goose. But then she
could not let go of the first girl.

The next girl tried to get
the first two girls away from the goose.
But something was holding
the first two girls together.
It was holding the next girl, too.
The three girls couldn't let go.

At last the farm boy went on
to the castle holding the golden goose.
The three girls bounced after him.

Later they saw a thief. "Stop,"
he said. "Stop, bad girls."

The thief tried to get the girls away from the boy and the goose. But then he could not let go of the girls. So the farm boy, the golden goose, the three girls, and the thief all went off to the castle together.

By the time the farm boy got to the castle, there were many people with him. There was a farmer, a farm girl, and a man who tried to get them away from the goose. And yes, there were the three girls and the thief. How people laughed to see them all going off to the castle together!

The princess was in the castle.
She sat by a window. She was so sad
she was about to cry. But she looked out
and saw the farm boy and the three girls.
She saw the thief, the farmer,
the farm girl, and the other man.
They all bounced back of the boy.
She looked up again and then—
the princess laughed!

The princess' father heard her.
He ran to find her. "You are laughing,"
he said. "You are laughing!"

Then he told all the people how happy he was to see the pretty princess laugh. He jumped up and down in the street. He was so happy.

"I laughed," said the princess. Then she laughed again, and again, and again. It was so good to laugh at last.

Later, the farm boy asked the princess to marry him, and the princess said, "Yes." Her father gave the princess and the farm boy many pretty things. The farm boy liked that. But he liked the laughing princess best of all.

Joe

"Joe," said his mother, "you will have to go to the store to get Bill a new ball. You lost his. Now you will have to get him a new one."

"I know I lost Bill's ball," said Joe. "But I don't want to get him a new one."

"Here are two of the dimes you worked for," said Joe's mother. Take them to the store and get a ball for Bill."

"I don't want to," Joe said again.

"You have to get it," said his mother.

Joe knew he had to go.

So Joe went up the street
to a store. It was a store he liked.
There were many things to play with
and to eat.

When Joe got to the store,
he saw some balls. There was one
just like the ball he had lost.

But there were so many other toys.
Joe didn't care about the balls.

There were many little toy animals.
Joe saw rabbits, dogs, kittens, and horses.
He liked all the little animals.

The man who owned the store knew Joe. He had seen Joe in the store at other times.

"What can I do for you, Joe?" he asked.

"I don't know," Joe said. "I like all the toy animals, but I don't know what I want."

"Well," the man said, "let me know when you are ready."

Joe saw other toys he liked. There were toy trucks and boats, balloons, whistles, so many things.

Joe didn't want to get Bill a ball.
He wanted a toy of his own.
What toy could he get for two dimes?

"Could I get a truck for two dimes?"
Joe asked himself.

The man who owned the store
came back. "Well," he said,
"what will it be?"

"I like all the toys," said Joe.
"But I like that truck best."

"Here, I will get it for you,"
said the man.

"No," said Joe. "I want to look at more toys."

"Oh, I see," said the man.

Then Joe saw some books. Joe liked books and there were all kinds of books here.

One of the books was about cowboys. Joe liked cowboys. "This must be a good book," he said to himself.

But Joe knew he could not get the book for two dimes.

Joe took the two dimes from his pocket and looked at them.

Then he looked at the toys. He looked
at the books. No, he could not get
a truck or a book for the two dimes.

Joe put the two dimes back
in his pocket.

Then he walked around the store
again. There were good things to eat
in the store, too. The little white cakes
looked so good!

Joe went over to the man
who owned the store. Joe asked,
"How many little white cakes
can I get for a dime?"

"Two," said the man.

Joe took one dime from his pocket.

The man saw the dime. "Do you want two cakes?" he asked.

Joe knew that he had to have two dimes to get the ball. If he got the cakes with one dime, he couldn't get the ball.

"Two cakes?" the man asked again.

"No," said Joe. "But I know they are good."

Then Joe saw some peanuts. He took a package of them to the man.

"Can I get peanuts for a dime?"
Joe asked.

"Yes," said the man. "The peanuts are a dime a package."

But Joe knew his two dimes were for the ball. He had to have **two** dimes. If he got the peanuts with one—

Joe put the peanuts back, but he wanted them. He wanted one of the toy animals, too. He wanted the truck and a book. He wanted the two cakes, but he did **not** want a ball for Bill.

Joe walked very slowly around the store. At last he knew what to get. He went to the man who owned the store. "I know what I am going to get," he said.

"So," said the man. "You are going to get something?"

"Yes," said Joe, "here are two dimes."

What do you think Joe got?
Why do you think so?

Weather Is Full of the Nicest Sounds

Weather is full
of the nicest sounds:
it sings
and rustles
and pings
and pounds
and hums
and tinkles
and strums
and twangs
and whishes
and sprinkles
and splishes
and bangs

and mumbles
and grumbles
and rumbles
and flashes
and CRASHES.
I wonder
if thunder
frightens a bee,
a mouse in her house,
a bird in a tree,
a bear
or a hare
or a fish in the sea?
Not me!

Aileen Fisher

Gus

On a little island with no trees lived a gull named Gus. Gus was not a happy bird. He didn't want to be a gull. He wanted to be some other kind of bird.

Other birds lived in pretty green trees, but Gus lived in wet brown grass.

Other birds lived on streets with houses and children. But there were no houses and children on the island. There were just other gulls.

Gus was not happy about the way
he looked. He was a big bird.
He wanted to be little like some
of the birds he had seen. He was brown.
He wanted to be red or yellow.
His bill was not like other birds' bills.
It looked like a hook.

Gus' mother knew how Gus felt.
She was very sad that Gus didn't want
to be a gull.

"Gus," his mother said, "some day
you will be happy you are not like
other birds. You can do things
that other birds can't do. You can go
way out over the river. If you were not
a big bird, you couldn't do that."

"And why don't you like to be
a brown bird?" she asked. "You live
in brown grass. You can hide
from animals that could hurt you.
If you were red or yellow,
they could see you in the grass."

"But why do I have to have a bill
like a hook?" asked Gus.

"Your bill helps you catch fish to eat,"
his mother said.

Gus wanted to be happy.
But gulls can't do the one thing
Gus wanted to do. Gus wanted to sing.
He had heard other birds sing,
so he wanted to sing, too.

He knew he had to be big and brown.
He knew he had to have a bill
like a hook. But he didn't know why
he couldn't sing.

So Gus tried to sing. He flew away
from the other gulls each day.
When no other birds were around,
he tried to sing.

He tried again and again. But all
he could do was make a big noise.
He just couldn't sing. So he didn't
try again.

He sat at home in the wet brown grass
on the island in the river.

Gus could not sing, and that was that.

One day Gus saw a little red boat
on the river close to the island.
The boat had a little boy in it.

Gus flew out to see the boy
in the boat.

Gus flew around and around the boy
in the little boat. But Gus didn't try
to sing. He didn't want the little boy
to know he couldn't sing.

So Gus just flew around and around.
He was happy to be with the little boy.
It was fun to have a new friend!

Then a big boat came down the river.
It was going fast. It was going so fast
that the man in the big boat didn't see
the little boat.

The boy saw the big boat and tried
to get his boat out of the way.
But it was too late.

When the big boat came by,
the little boat went over. The boy fell
into the water.

Gus was scared. He wanted to help
the boy. But how could he? He
couldn't get the boy out of the water.

Then he knew what he could do.
He began to make the big noise
he could make when he tried to sing.

Gus wanted the man on the big boat
to see the little boy. The noise Gus made
was not pretty, but the man heard it.
He looked at Gus. Then he saw the boy
floating in the water.

He took his boat over to the boy.
He helped the boy get into it.

The man then set the little boat up
in the water. Next he helped the boy
get from the big boat into the little boat.
   The boy was wet all over,
but he was all right. Each of the boats
went on down the river and Gus flew
home.
   Gus was happy that night.
He had helped the little boy in the boat.
Now he knew a gull could do good things,
too. He liked his island in the river.
He was happy to be a gull.
   After that, Gus didn't try
to sing again.

River, River

Have you ever seen a river?
If you have, then you know
that rivers are on the go.

Each river takes its own trip.
Some rivers hurry on their way.
Some go slowly. No two rivers
are the same.

As you look at a river, you can see
the water going by you. You may want
to know where it comes from and
where it is going.

The river can't tell you. It can't
talk. If a river could talk,
it could tell you many things
about its trip.

Here is a story one river could tell
about its trip:

I began in the mountains.
At first I was ice and snow.
Then the rain and sun made the ice
and snow into water. The water
began to run down the mountain.

As the water ran down the mountain,
more water ran with it.
At last there was enough water to be
a little stream. That is how
I began.

Many people came to the stream
to fish in my waters. Animals came
for water. Some people came
just to look at the little stream.

There were many other little streams. We met as we ran down the mountain. I became a very big stream. The banks of the stream were not big enough to hold me. They were cut back by the water so that I could go on down the mountain.

Soon I was big enough to be a river. On and on I went. I went by quiet farms. The farmers took some of me to water their farms. Children played on my banks.

Soon I went by little towns.
People in the towns took water
for many things. I helped boats
take people and goods from town
to town.

I went by a big city.
The city was close to the sea.
I helped big boats take people
from the city out to sea.

The people were going to take trips over the sea. But my trip was over. Into the sea I ran.

I was not sad that my trip was over. Up in the mountains more rain and snow were falling. More water was falling down the mountain to the sea.

Louis Makes A New Friend

Louis lived by a little stream.
There were other streams close by.
But Louis knew of just one, and that was
the one by his house.
 Louis lived with his father
and mother and his three sisters
in a little brown house. There were
just three houses on Louis' street.
Each house looked the same.
It was a quiet street with farms
all around.

There was a school on Louis' street. It was brown like the houses on the street. Louis was six, so he went to school.

Louis liked school, but he liked to play, too. He liked to play by the stream.

One day Louis was playing on one bank of the stream. On the other bank he saw Freddy.

Freddy didn't go to school. He was just five. He didn't live on Louis' street. He lived in a big house on a farm. He didn't have many friends. When Louis saw Freddy, he was playing by himself. He was looking for something on the bank of the stream.

Louis had not played with Freddy, but he had met him. Now he wanted to go over to talk with him.

"We could have fun playing together," Louis said to himself.

Then Louis heard a splash.
He looked down. He couldn't see
anything in the water.

Louis heard something splash again.
Now Louis saw what Freddy was trying
to do. He was trying to catch one
of the little frogs on the bank. The frogs
didn't want Freddy to catch them,
so they jumped into the stream. Splash!
There went a frog into the stream.

Louis knew how to catch frogs.
At times he got one just for fun.
Then he let it go again. The frogs here
were not the kind to eat.

Then Freddy saw a frog jump.

He tried to catch it, too. But it got away into the stream. Louis laughed.

Freddy looked around when he heard Louis laugh. Then he saw Louis on the other bank. "Go away," he said.

Louis didn't say anything. He knew he could play on the bank if he wanted to. Freddy didn't own the stream.

Louis said, "I am not doing anything to you. I can stay here if I want to."

He looked down in the grass and said, "And I can catch a frog. Do you want to see me?"

"I want to see you try," said Freddy.

Louis liked to show what he could do. He looked down in the grass and saw two frogs. He got one frog right away. Then he got the other one.

"See, here are two frogs," said Louis. Then he let the frogs go. There were two splashes as they jumped into the stream.

Freddy laughed and laughed. "Come and show me how to catch them," he said.

Louis didn't want Freddy to tell him
to go away again. So he said,
"I am not going over there if I am not
your friend."

"I want you to be my friend,"
said Freddy. "Now will you come on
over here?"

So Louis ran over to the other bank.
He was very happy.

Louis showed Freddy how to catch
frogs. Each frog Freddy tried
to catch got away. Freddy tried
and tried, but he couldn't catch a frog.

"You catch one for me," Freddy said
at last. "And don't let it go next time.
I want one to take home for a pet."

"Why do you want a frog?"
asked Louis. "Frogs are not good pets."

"My frog will be," said Freddy.

Louis laughed. He didn't know why
Freddy wanted a frog for a pet.
But he got a frog for his new friend.

Freddy looked at the frog. He looked at Louis. "I have some candy in my pocket," he said. "Do you want some? I will give it to you for the frog."

Louis took the candy. "Thank you. I like candy," he said.

Both boys were happy. Freddy wanted a frog. Now he had one. And Louis liked all kinds of candy. Now he had some.

Best of all, the two boys were friends.

Louis was eating the candy when he got home.

"Where did you get the candy, Louis?" his mother asked.

Louis laughed and said, "A frog got it for me."

Ring Around the World

Ring around the world
Taking hands together
All across the temperate
And the torrid weather.
Past the royal palm trees
By the ocean sand
Make a ring around the world
Taking each other's hand;
In the valleys, on the hill,
Over the prairie spaces,
There's a ring around the world
Made of children's friendly faces.
Annette Wynne

Crick-Crick

Sam and Ted were very good friends. They walked to school together, and after school they played together.

They liked to be make-believe people. Sometimes they were cowboys or astronauts or policemen or doctors.

The boys had many toys to play with. They liked to ride their bikes and to play ball.

One day Sam didn't come to school. After school Ted went to his house.

Sam's mother said, "Sam hurt his leg last night, Ted. He must stay off his leg. He can't go to school, and he can't go out to play. But you can come here to play with him."

"Can I see Sam, now?" asked Ted.

"No," said Sam's mother.
"He is sleeping, but come back later, Ted. He wants to see you."

So Ted went home. He played ball. He went for a ride on his bike, but Ted was very sad. It was no fun to play by himself.

Soon Ted's father came home. He saw Ted playing by himself. "Where is Sam?" he asked. "Did you two have a fight?"

"No," said Ted. "Sam can't play. He hurt his leg and has to stay in bed."

"That's too bad," said Ted's father. "But you can go to Sam's house to see him, can't you? I will go with you, and we can take him something to play with."

"That will be fun," said Ted. "When can we get something for Sam?"

"Very soon," said Ted's father.

The next day Ted ran home from school. "Is Dad here, Mother?" he asked.

"No, Ted," she said. "But he will be here soon."

Ted went to the window over and over again, but he didn't see his father. At last Ted heard a noise, and soon his dad came into the house. Ted ran to see him but he didn't see a package. "You didn't get anything for Sam," he said.

"Yes, I did," Ted's father said. He took a little package from his pocket.

"This is for Sam," he said. "I know he will like it and so will you."

"What is it?" asked Ted.

"You will see it when we get to Sam's house. Let's take it to him now," said Ted's father.

"Where did you get it, Dad?" asked Ted.

"I got it at a little store on the street where I work. The store is owned by a man who comes from far away. He said it is something many boys have where he lived before."

Ted and his father went to Sam's house. Sam was very happy to see them. Ted showed Sam the little package.

"This is for you," he said.

"Now you have a new pet, Sam," said Ted's father.

"A pet?" asked Sam.

"Yes, you will see," said Ted's father.

So Sam looked in the package. He saw a very little cage. In the cage was something black.

"It is a cricket," said Ted's father.

Sam and Ted looked at the cricket. They liked it. It was so little, and it looked so scared. Sam said, "Hello, little cricket. Don't be scared. I have a big cage that is just right for you."

Then Sam asked, "What can we name him?"

"Let's call him Crick-Crick," said Ted.

"Crick-Crick will sing for you when you put the lights out at night." said Ted's father.

"Will he?" asked Sam.

"Yes, you will see. Crickets sing when it is dark and quiet."

Sam put the cage by his bed. He said, "Crick-Crick can sing me to sleep."

The next day Ted went to Sam's house as soon as school was out.

"Did Crick-Crick sing last night, Sam?" Ted asked.

"Yes he did," said Sam. "He will sing for you, too."

"Can we make him sing now?" asked Ted.

"Yes," said Sam, "we can put something over his cage so it will be dark. If we are very quiet the cricket will sing for us."

"Good," said Ted. "Let's try to get him to sing."

When Crick-Crick's cage was dark and quiet, he began to sing. "Crick, crick, crick, crick, crick, crick."

It was a pretty little noise. Sam and Ted laughed.

"I want to see Crick-Crick sing," said Sam. "Let's look at him."

"Oh, no," said Ted. "He won't sing if we look at him. A cricket won't sing in the light."

"How do you know?" asked Sam.

"Dad told me," said Ted. "He told me how a cricket sings, too. It doesn't sing with its mouth."

"How does it sing then?" asked Sam.

"It sings with its wings," said Ted.

"How can a cricket sing with its wings?" asked Sam.

"It rubs them together and they make noise," said Ted. "Crickets are not like other pets."

"I am so happy to have Crick-Crick for a pet," said Sam. "We can play together each day. At night when it is dark, my cricket will sing me to sleep."

"I can get some books about crickets at school," said Ted. "Then we will know how to take care of your new pet. When you come back to school, Crick-Crick can come with you."

"No one will have a pet like Crick-Crick," said Sam.

A Cricket

In a matchbox
is a cricket
with a patent-leather shine.
It's at Peter's
and he's printed
MISTER CRICKET on a sign.

In a fruit jar
that is open,
with a leaf on which to dine,
is a cricket
that is Kathy's
and she thinks it's very fine.

Nothing's gayer
than a cricket.
Nothing's louder after nine!
But my mother
thinks a thicket
is the nicest place for mine.

Aileen Fisher

The Shoemaker and the Elves

There was a time when a shoemaker and his wife had a little store.
They were good people.
They worked hard. They were old and had very little money.

One day the shoemaker said, "Wife, things are very bad for us. We have no more money. And we have no shoes to sell."

"You can make new shoes," said his wife.

"But I have leather for just one pair," said the shoemaker. "I will make the last pair. If we don't sell them, I don't know what we will do."

The shoemaker began to cut the leather. He wanted the shoes to be very pretty.

He said to his wife, "I will make the shoes in the morning."

The next morning when the shoemaker went to make the shoes, the leather was not there. But he saw a pair of new shoes. They were very pretty!

"Who could have made the shoes?" asked his wife. "There was no one in the store last night."

"I don't know," said the shoemaker. "But I didn't."

Just then a man came into the store.

"What pretty shoes!" he said.
"I want them. Here is the money."

Then the shoemaker had enough money to get leather for **two** pairs of shoes.

The little old shoemaker was happy. He went to get more leather.

That night the shoemaker cut the leather for two more pairs of shoes. He was going to make the shoes the next day.

The next morning there were two pairs of pretty shoes in his store.

"Wife," he said, "come here.
Look at the pretty shoes.
Who made them?"

"I don't know," said his wife.
"I don't know."

Soon a man came into the store.
He saw the new shoes.

"I want both pairs," he said.
"Will you sell them to me?"

"Oh, yes," said the shoemaker.
"I am very happy that you like them."

The shoemaker got enough money
from the man to get leather for six pairs
of shoes.

The shoemaker and his wife
were so happy!

That night the shoemaker cut
the leather for six pairs of shoes.
But again he did not make the shoes.

His wife said, "Let's not
go to sleep now. Let's stay up late to see
who comes to make the shoes."

So they went into the store.
They hid where no one
could see them.
　　Late that night they saw a light
at the window. They heard a noise.
It was like children laughing.
　　Soon the shoemaker and his wife
saw two little elves at the window.
The little elves came into the store
and went right to work. They began
to make shoes.

"Look!" said the wife. "Little elves have come here each night.
They have made the pretty shoes, but they have no suits."

"And no shoes," said the shoemaker.

Soon the elves had made six more pairs of shoes. The elves put the shoes out for people to see them. Then they went out the window like a light going out.

The shoemaker's wife said, "The little elves were very good to us. Let's do something for them. I will make them some little suits."

"And I will make little shoes for them," said the shoemaker.

The next day many people came
to the store. But the shoemaker took time
to make the two little pairs of red shoes.
His wife made two little green suits.

That night the shoemaker and his wife
put the little suits and the little shoes
where the elves could see them.
They stayed up again to see the elves.

Soon there was a light at the window.
There was the noise again,
like children laughing.

The two little elves came into the store.

They laughed and laughed when they saw the little green suits and the red shoes.

Then they put on the little green suits and the little red shoes. They ran around the store. They jumped up and down. They played and played together.

How happy the little elves were!

But soon they went out the window again, like a light going out.

The little elves didn't come back to the shoemaker's store. They didn't have to come back.

Now the shoemaker had enough money to get more leather for more shoes. People came from all around to his store. He and his wife were happy ever after.

And the elves were happy, too.

Elves and Apple Trees

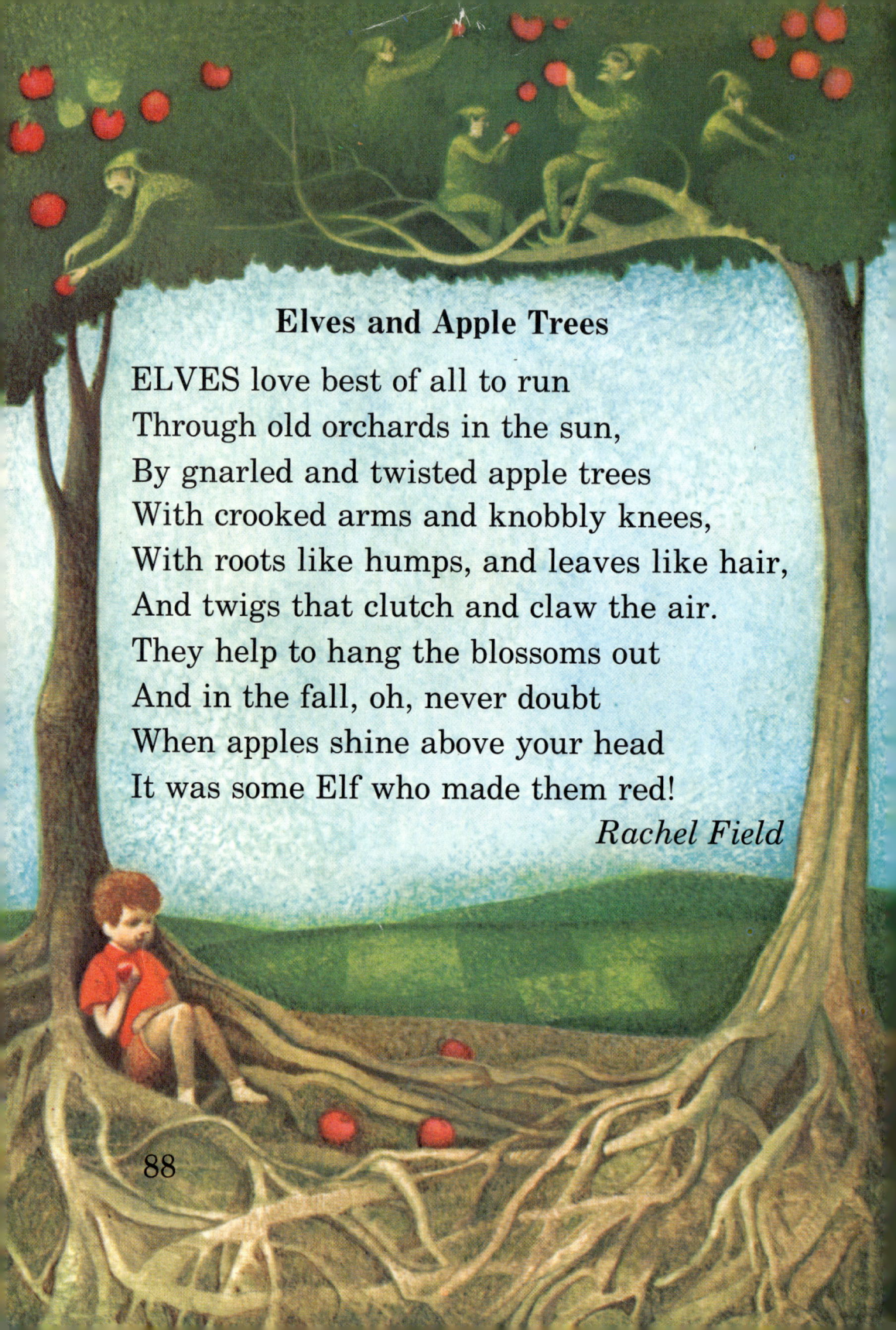

ELVES love best of all to run
Through old orchards in the sun,
By gnarled and twisted apple trees
With crooked arms and knobbly knees,
With roots like humps, and leaves like hair,
And twigs that clutch and claw the air.
They help to hang the blossoms out
And in the fall, oh, never doubt
When apples shine above your head
It was some Elf who made them red!

Rachel Field

Peter's Trip to the Bay

Peter Hall lived close to a river.
His father had a fishing boat. Each day
Mr. Hall took the boat down the river
to a big bay. In the bay he got
many fish to sell.

Peter wanted to go fishing
with his father. He liked the fishing boat,
and he wanted to help his father.
But the one thing Peter wanted
more than to fish was to see
some frogmen.

Peter's father had told him about the frogmen. They went to school at a naval station on the bay.
His father had seen them many times when he was fishing.

But Peter had not seen the frogmen. He had not been out to the bay. But his father said, "We will go as soon as school is out, Peter."

Now school was out, and Peter was going on the boat the next morning.

"Maybe I will get to see the frogmen," Peter said.

Peter had a book about frogmen.
The book showed the frogmen
in their diving suits.

Peter took the book to his father.
He showed his father the pictures.

Then he asked, "Do the frogmen
at the naval station look like the frogmen
in the book?"

"Yes," said Mr. Hall. "They have suits
that do not let them get wet. They have
tanks on their backs to give them air
when they swim underwater."

Then Mr. Hall said, "Frogmen
can stay underwater for a very long time.
I have heard about four frogmen
who stayed underwater for four days."

"Four days?" asked Peter.

"Yes," said Mr. Hall. "Frogmen work underwater. They must stay underwater a long time to do their work."

"What kind of work do they do?" asked Peter.

Mr. Hall said, "Frogmen help people who have to have help in the water. Did you know that frogmen help astronauts?"

"Here is a picture of a frogman with an astronaut after splash-down," said Peter.

"Yes," said Mr. Hall. "Frogmen are the first ones to get to the astronauts when they splash down. They help the astronauts into the airplane that comes for them."

"Will we see some frogmen when we go out in the boat?" asked Peter.

"I don't know," said Mr. Hall. "But you can see the naval station where the frogmen live."

Peter didn't want to go to sleep that night. He took his book about frogmen to bed with him and looked at it again. Soon Peter was sleeping.

The next morning Peter's mother got a big lunch ready. Mr. Hall got the boat ready. Peter helped put things on the boat.

At last Peter was on his way down the river to the bay. Mr. Hall ran the boat close to the shore of the bay. He wanted Peter to see the houses and fishing boats by the shore.

Soon Mr. Hall said, "Look over there where all the boats are, Peter. That's the naval station I told you about."

"Are the frogmen there?" asked Peter.

"Yes," said his father.

Then Peter said, "Let's go over to the naval station now. I want to see the frogmen. Please, Daddy!"

"We can't go to the naval station now, Peter," said Mr. Hall. "We have to catch fish. You will see the frogmen some other time."

The boat went on out into the bay, but Peter didn't want to fish now. He wanted to go to the naval station.

Some gulls flew over the boat. Peter liked their big wings, and he liked the noise they made.

Then the boat began to go more slowly. "This is where we will fish," his father said.

Peter's father had work to do and Peter helped him. Soon they got their first fish and Peter was happy again. He liked fishing, but he **did** want to see the frogmen.

Peter and the Frogmen

Peter and his father had been fishing all morning when Peter saw something splash up out of the water. "Daddy," said Peter, "what is that over there? Is it a submarine?"

"Yes, Peter. That's a submarine from the naval station," said Mr. Hall.

"What is it doing here?" asked Peter. "Why did it come up out of the water?"

"I don't know, Peter," said Mr. Hall.

Then he said, "Here, Peter, help me with the fish."

Peter did what his father told him to do. Then he heard an airplane. It flew slowly around the submarine.

A man jumped from the airplane. Then other men jumped one at a time.

"Look, Daddy," said Peter. "The men are jumping from the airplane."

Soon all the men were in the water. Peter could see that they had on diving suits. And they had tanks on their backs. They were frogmen!

"Daddy, Daddy," said Peter. "Look at the frogmen! Look at their diving suits! We got to see them after all!"

"Yes, Peter," said Mr. Hall.

"I'm happy that you got to see them."

Then the frogmen went underwater, and Peter could not see them. He wanted to know what they were doing.
But the frogmen stayed underwater.

Peter looked and looked at the water. At last he saw a frogman come up. Then more frogmen came up. They went to the submarine and got on it.

"Look," said Peter. "The frogmen are getting on the submarine."

"Frogmen work with submarines," said Peter's father. "A submarine can take them close to the shore.

Then the frogmen swim to shore,
do their work, and go back
to the submarine."

"So that's why the submarine
was here," said Peter.

"Yes," said Mr. Hall. "It was here
to get the frogmen."

"But they didn't come
in the submarine," said Peter.

"No," said Mr. Hall.
"Frogmen can jump into the water
from airplanes. Then they can swim
to submarines or other boats
when their work is over."

"Come now, Peter," said Mr. Hall,
"let's get on with the work
we have to do."

So Peter and his father began
to work again.

The submarine did not go away
after the frogmen got on it. Later
some men from the submarine
put a little boat into the water.

The men went around and around
in the little boat.

"What are the men in the boat doing?"
asked Peter.

"They are looking for something,"
said his father.

Then the airplane came back.
It went around and around, too.

Peter was looking at the airplane
when he heard a noise close to the boat.

He looked over and saw two men.
One was calling to Peter's father.

"Peter, that's two of the frogmen,"
Mr. Hall said. "One of them
must be hurt." He waved to the men and
then ran the boat to them
as fast as he could.

Peter and Mr. Hall helped
the frogmen into the boat.

"My friend is hurt,"
said one of the frogmen.

"Put him down here," said Mr. Hall.

Then Mr. Hall helped the frogman
take off some of his diving suit
so that he could get air.

"It was a good thing you saw us," said the frogman. "I hurt my back when I jumped from the airplane. We called to the other frogmen, but no one heard us. The men on the submarine and the men in the airplane didn't see us."

"Peter heard you," Mr. Hall said. "I am Ben Hall, and this is Peter. He is the one who heard you calling. Now we must get the men in the airplane to see us so they will see you, too." "Then they can let the men on the submarine know you are here."

Peter and Mr. Hall got something white and began to wave it in the air.

The men on the airplane flew over them and saw the boat and the frogmen. Then the airplane went away.

"They saw us," said a frogman. "They will have a boat come for us."

"I can take you to the naval station," said Mr. Hall.

"Good. Please take us there as soon as you can," said the other frogman.

Soon they were on their way.

Peter talked with the frogmen again. He said, "Please tell me all about frogmen. I want to be a frogman someday and swim underwater."

The men told Peter about their work.
They told him what it is like
to jump from an airplane. They told him
how they stay underwater.
"You must know many things to be
a frogman," they said. "Work hard
in school and you will be
a good frogman."

"I will try," said Peter.

Soon the fishing boat came close
to the naval station.

"You can take the boat over there,"
said one of the frogmen to Peter's father.

When the boat came into the station,
a man came out to the boat.

"What happened?" he asked.
"We heard you were on a fishing boat."

One frogman said, "I got hurt as I jumped. I couldn't get to the submarine."

"I stayed with him," said the other frogman. "And Mr. Hall and Peter helped us."

"We all thank you, Mr. Hall," said the man. "It was a good thing you happened to be there."

Then the other frogman said, "And we have a new frogman for you. Peter wants to be one someday."

"Well," said the man, "I know he will make a very good frogman."

Then Peter said, "I want to see the other frogmen. I want to see the boats and all the things here at the naval station."

"We will be happy to have you come to see us," said the man.

"When can we come back, Daddy?" asked Peter.

"We will come soon, Peter," said Mr. Hall. "But it is late now. We must go home."

Peter waved to the frogmen as he and his father went to their boat. The frogmen waved back.

Peter was a happy boy that night.

When he got home, he told his mother about all the things that had happened to him. He told her that now he had two frogmen for his friends.

His mother said, "Peter, you are a good boy. And if you want to be a frogman someday, I know you will be a good one."

"I will try to be!" said Peter.

Then Peter got his book about frogmen. He took the book to bed with him. As he went to sleep, he could see himself in a diving suit. He was helping an astronaut who had just splashed down.

Truck-Riding Hen

Hazel is a little red hen. She lives on Mr. Terry's farm.

Many people know about Hazel. There was a story about her in the newspaper. Hazel did something very brave.

Mr. Terry went to town each day to work. He went in his truck.

Hazel saw Mr. Terry go away each day. She wanted to go with him. She wanted to take a truck ride. She wanted to see things she couldn't see on the farm.

So one morning Hazel jumped on a spring under the truck. She just sat there. No one saw her. No one heard her.

Mr. Terry didn't know Hazel was there. When he was ready to go to work, he got in the truck.

The truck made a very big noise. Hazel didn't like the noise. She was very scared. Then the truck began to go very fast. That scared Hazel, too. But Hazel knew she had to be brave. She had to hold on to the spring.

The truck bounced and bounced. Each time the truck bounced, Hazel did too. She bounced this way and that way. But she didn't let go of the spring.

At last the truck stopped.
Mr. Terry got out and went off to work.
Hazel looked around. She didn't know
where she was. She didn't know
where to go. She didn't know what to do.
There was no one to help her.
Hazel stayed on the spring all day.
When Mr. Terry came back
to the truck, he saw Hazel and he laughed.
"What are you doing here, Hazel?"
he said.
Hazel just sat there on the spring.
Mr. Terry took Hazel off the spring and
put her in the back of the truck.
Then he got in the truck.
Soon they were on their way home.

When they got to the farm, Mr. Terry put Hazel in the barn. "Hazel won't go for another ride," he said.

The next morning Hazel got on the spring again. Hazel wanted to ride to town. She wanted to see the things she had not seen the other time.

Mr. Terry didn't know Hazel was on the truck.

When he got to town he went to work. Hazel jumped down from the truck. She walked all around. But she stayed by the truck.

There were so many cars and trucks. There were so many people.

A man saw Hazel. He said, "Look, Mr. Terry. There is a hen over there by your truck. Is she your hen?"

"Yes," said Mr. Terry. "That's Hazel."

Mr. Terry got Hazel and put her in the back of the truck.

He said, "Hazel, you must stop riding to town with me. The streets here are not like the farm. The cars and trucks go very fast. You will get hurt."

Hazel liked the truck rides, and she liked to be in town.

So the next day Hazel got on the spring one more time. Soon Mr. Terry got in the truck and Hazel was happy. She knew she was on the way to town again.

Mr. Terry stopped for a red light. He was going fast when he stopped.

Hazel bounced off the spring. Cars and trucks were hurrying up and down the street.

Hazel didn't know what to do.
She began to walk one way,
but there were too many cars.
   She began to walk another way.
There were too many cars
that way, too.
   Then a policeman saw Hazel.
He stopped the cars and trucks
so that Hazel could get out of the way.
   Hazel was so scared! She wanted
to go back to the farm. She didn't know
where Mr. Terry and the truck were.
Many people saw Hazel and
laughed at her.

Hazel didn't know that Mr. Terry was on the way back to get her.
He had seen Hazel after she fell off the spring. He stopped the truck as soon as he could and went back to get her.

He came back to where Hazel had bounced off the spring. When he saw the people laughing, he knew Hazel was all right.

Hazel was very happy to see Mr. Terry. She was very happy when he put her in the back of the truck and took her to the farm.

The next morning she didn't get up on the spring. Mr. Terry looked under the truck, but Hazel was not there.

That day Mr. Terry told some friends at work about Hazel's three truck rides. A newspaperman heard about them. He went to the farm to take Hazel's picture. Then he put Hazel's picture in the newspaper with a story about her. The newspaperman called Hazel "a truck-riding hen."

Hazel has not had a ride to town again. But who knows? Hazel took three truck rides. She may take another one someday.

Rosa

Rosa loved animals. She liked cats and dogs and birds and rabbits. She liked all kinds of animals.

Rosa did not get to see many animals. There were no animals where Rosa lived.

Rosa lived in an apartment house in a big city. She had many brothers and sisters. Their apartment was not big enough for all the children and a pet, too! If the apartment **were** big, Rosa couldn't have a pet. There could be no pets in Rosa's apartment house.

Rosa's pets were make-believe pets.
She had books about animals.
She cut out pictures of animals.
She put some of the pictures
over her bed.

Rosa liked her make-believe pets,
but wanted an animal of her own.

It was raining hard one day
as Rosa was on her way home from school.
When Rosa got to her street, she saw
a little yellow kitten.

The kitten was wet all over. It was
just a baby. "You must be lost,
little kitten," said Rosa.

Rosa was going to walk away.
But she couldn't. She couldn't let
the little kitten stay there in the rain.

"It could get sick if I let it stay here,"
she said.

So she put the kitten under her coat
and took it home.

Rosa got a box and put the kitten
in it. Her mother saw her.

"What do you have there, Rosa?"
asked her mother.

"Oh, Mother," said Rosa. "I have
a little kitten. It is wet all over.
It was lost. I want to take care of it,
so it will not get sick."

"I know you could take care of it, Rosa," said her mother.
"But you can't keep the kitten. You know we can't have pets in the apartment. It is a good kitten, but you will have to put it back where you got it."

"Please, Mother," said Rosa. "Please let me keep it. The kitten will get sick if it has to stay out in the rain. I want to take care of it."

"I know you do. But we can't have a kitten here, Rosa," said her mother.

"Please, Mother," said Rosa.

"No, Rosa," said her mother. "You can't keep the kitten. Why don't you take it to school. Give it to one of your friends."

That night Rosa played with the kitten. She loved her pet. The next day Rosa had to take the kitten to school. She had to give it to a girl she knew.

Three days later Rosa came home with another pet. This time it was a bird, and it was hurt.

"Here you are with another pet, Rosa," said her mother. "What will I do with you?"

"Mother, this little bird was on the street. It was hurt. Look at its wing. I don't know how it got hurt."

"What can you do for the bird?" asked her mother.

"I can take care of it," said Rosa. "We can get a little cage and put it in the window."

"A little cage?" said her mother.
"How can you get a cage?
You don't have money for a cage."

"Oh, Mother. I'll work for the money.
"I'll get it. I know I will. Please
let me keep the bird."

"Rosa, I have told you that we
can't have a pet here."

"Let me keep the bird
for a day or two. Just a day or two,"
said Rosa. "Then I'll give it away.
I'll take it to school."

"We will see, Rosa. It is late.
Do your school work. We can talk
about the bird later," said her mother.

Rosa didn't want to do her work for school. But she put the bird in a box and did her work.

The next day Rosa ran home from school. She wanted to see her bird. She was so happy to have a pet at last.

When Rosa got home, she went to the box where she had put the bird. The bird was not there.

"Mother! Mother!" called Rosa. "Where is my bird? What happened to my bird?"

"Your bird, Rosa?" asked her mother. "It is not here."

"Not here?" said Rosa.

"No, it is not here. I had to give it away. It is too bad, Rosa. But you knew we couldn't keep it."

Rosa cried and cried. Other boys and girls had pets. Rosa wanted a pet, too.

Rosa's mother said, "Don't cry, Rosa. One day we will live where you can have a pet. You can't have one here, but you will have one someday."

After that Rosa didn't come home with animals again. But she got more books and pictures about animals. Rosa knew that for now her pets had to be make-believe.

The Black Puppy

One day Rosa came home from school
a new way. She walked down
another street.
She saw a store with the word PETS
on the window. She stopped
at the window to see the pets.
There were kittens and rabbits
and birds in the store. There was
a little black puppy, too.
Rosa stayed at the window
for a long time. How pretty
the animals were!

It was late when she got home.

"Where were you, Rosa?" asked her mother.

"Oh, Mother, I saw some animals—many animals—in a store," said Rosa.

"Animals again, Rosa?" said her mother. "Why do you love animals?"

"I don't know, Mother," said Rosa. "I just do."

The next day Rosa walked by the pet store again. She went by it the day after that and the day after that.

One day when Rosa walked
by the pet store some people
were going in. She went with them.

Rosa went from cage to cage.
It was like being in a make-believe store.
All the animals from the books
were there.

The man who owned the store
saw Rosa. He said, "May I help you?
Have you come to get a pet?"

"No. No, I can't have a pet. I live
in an apartment," said Rosa.
"My mother says that we can't have
animals there."

"Too bad," said the man.
"A good little girl like you
with no pet! Too bad!"

Then Rosa said, "Some day we won't live in a big city. Then I am going to have a pet."

"Good," said the man. "I know you will take good care of your pet when you get it."

"I can't have a pet of my own now, but I can come to see your animals," said Rosa. "I love all of them, but I love the little black puppy best."

"The black puppy?" asked the man. "I can't sell him. No one likes him."

"I do," said Rosa. "But I can't have him. One day I'll have a puppy or a kitten or a bird. But I can't have one now."

"I know what we can do,"
said the man. "I am old now. I have
lots of animals. You could help me
take care of them. You could come
after school and help me."

"Could I?" asked Rosa.
She was very happy.

"I will help you take care
of all the animals if my mother
will let me," she said.

Then Rosa looked at the puppy again.
"Will the black puppy be here?"
she asked.

"I will give you the black puppy,"
said the man. "You can have him
for helping me. You can keep him here."

"Oh," said Rosa. "I will ask my mother to let me help you. I know she will let me."

When Rosa got home, she told her mother about the pet shop. "May I help there?" she asked.

"If it will make you happy to take care of the animals, Rosa, it is all right," her mother said.

No little girl in the big city was as happy as Rosa that night. A puppy of her own and so many animals to love!

Rosa didn't have to have make-believe pets after that. No one in her school had as many pets as Rosa. She loved each one of her pets, and each one of them loved her.

Jump or Jiggle

Frogs jump
Caterpillars hump

Worms wiggle
Bugs jiggle

Rabbits hop
Horses clop

Snakes slide
Sea gulls glide

Mice creep
Deer leap

Puppies bounce
Kittens pounce

Lions stalk—
But—
I walk!

Evelyn Beyer

The Saggy Baggy Elephant

A happy little elephant lived far away
where there were many animals.
He liked to dance. He liked to go
one-two-three-kick, one-two-three-kick.

Elephants are very big animals.
Baby elephants are big, too. So each time
the little elephant danced
the earth bounced. Sometimes
when he went one-two-three-kick,
he kicked a tree down.

One day the little elephant met a bird.
The bird had not seen an elephant before
—and an elephant that **danced** at that!

"Why do you make the earth bounce?
Why do you kick down the trees?"
asked the bird. "What kind of animal
are you?"

"I don't know what kind of animal
I am," said the little elephant.
"I don't have a mother or a father.
I don't have a sister or a brother."

Then the little elephant said, "I like
to dance. I go one-two-three-kick.
My name is Sooki. Don't you like
my name? It fits me!"

"If your name fits you, it is all
that does," said the bird. "Your mouth
is too big, and your skin is
very, very big for you.

"No, Sooki is not a good name for you," the bird said. "Saggy Baggy is the best name for you. Your skin is all saggy and baggy. Your skin does not fit you."

Sooki looked at himself. The bird was right. His skin was saggy and baggy. It was too big. It was just too big!

"I want to make my skin fit me, but I don't know how. What can I do?" asked Sooki.

"I can't tell you that," said the bird. "I have not seen an animal like you."

The little elephant looked at his saggy,
baggy skin. He wanted to do away
with all the wrinkles. He tried and tried
to make his skin fit.

The more he tried to get out the
wrinkles, the more wrinkles there were.
The bird laughed at him.

Just then a tiger came walking by.
His skin didn't have wrinkles.
It fitted him all over.

Sooki said, "Tiger, please tell me
why your skin fits you so well.
The bird said my skin is saggy and baggy.
I want my skin to fit like yours."

"My skin was not ever baggy like yours," said the tiger. "You see, I walk and run a lot. That must be it."

Then the tiger said, "You must run and walk more, my friend. That will help. Or I can eat away some of your wrinkles for you."

"Oh, no," said Sooki. "Don't eat me. I love to run. Just look at me!"

Sooki ran so fast he was soon far away from the tiger. He ran this way and that way. He did many kinds of tricks, but was as saggy and as baggy as ever.

Later Sooki went down to the river
to get some water. He saw the bird again.
The bird laughed more and more.

"I ran and walked a lot," said Sooki.
"That didn't help at all.
Now I don't know what to do."

"Get in the water," said the bird.
"Maybe it will make your skin fit."
So Sooki went into the water.

"I will go where no one will see
my saggy, baggy skin," Sooki said
to himself.

When he got out of the water,
he heard a big noise.
He looked around and saw a lion.

"I want something to eat," said the lion. "I have not had anything to eat all day. I could eat an **elephant**."

He began to walk over to Sooki.

"Oh!" Sooki said to himself. "I will not have saggy, baggy skin after this. The lion will do away with my wrinkles."

Sooki began to cry. Just as he did, he heard a big noise. The earth began to bounce. Many big elephants ran at the lion.

The lion jumped up in the air. He ran away in a big hurry.

Sooki looked up. All the big elephants smiled at him. They had saggy, baggy skin, too. Sooki smiled at them. They were the best-looking animals he had ever seen.

"I wish I looked just like you," he said.

"You do," laughed the big elephants.

"You are a very pretty little elephant."

Sooki was so happy he began to dance again. "One-two-three-kick, one-two-three-kick," he went.

The bird saw Sooki. He saw all the big brave elephants, too. All the elephants danced like Sooki, but this time the bird didn't laugh. **No** one ever laughed at Sooki again.

The Orange Tree

Pepita was to have a birthday soon, and she was happy about it. She walked down the street, by the white houses. She was singing as she walked:

"A birthday, a birthday,
I am going to have a birthday!"
All Pepita's friends in the white houses heard her singing. So they knew about the birthday.

Pepita bounced in and out of the stores, singing as she went:
"A birthday, a birthday,
I am going to have a birthday!"

Her friends in the stores laughed to see Pepita so happy. "What do you want for your birthday, Pepita?" they asked.

Pepita said, "An orange tree."
Each time she was asked, she said, "An orange tree. I want an orange tree of my very own."

Then Pepita's friends laughed. "An orange tree!" they said. "Why do you want an orange tree?"

"I just want one," said Pepita.

When she had bounced out again, Pepita's friends looked at each other and said, "An orange tree! When Pepita sees what I have for her birthday, she will not want an orange tree."

That is how things went at home, too, and with the children Pepita knew. They all asked, "What do you want for your birthday?"

Pepita said to each one, "An orange tree." They just laughed.

Then they said to each other,
"Why does she want an orange tree?
When Pepita sees what I have for her,
she won't want an old orange tree."

All but one of Pepita's friends
said that. Manolo didn't say it at all.
Manolo knew why she wanted
an orange tree. He and Pepita talked
and talked about it.

They talked about the fun they could
have playing around the orange tree.
Pepita said, "My tree will have
oranges on it, too. I will take the oranges
to the store and sell them. I will get
a hat for your donkey with the money!"

"Oh, my donkey will like that!"
laughed Manolo. "So will I!"
Pepita laughed. What fun they
could have with the donkey and its hat!

Manolo and his donkey had to work
very hard. They had to work hard to get
enough to eat. Manolo didn't have money
to get something for Pepita's birthday.
That was all right with Pepita.
She knew there were others
who could give her the orange tree.
That was all she wanted.

At last it was Pepita's birthday.
Pepita bounced out of bed
as soon as the sun came up.

"A birthday, a birthday, I have a birthday!" said Pepita as she ran to the window. She heard the birds singing. She saw the yellow sun and the blue sea.

"Oh," cried Pepita, "What a good day for a birthday. What a good, good day to plant my orange tree."

Mama was up, but Papa was sleeping. Pepita got up on the big bed and bounced up and down. "Get up, Papa," she said. "Get up. It is time to plant my orange tree."

"Orange tree!" said Pepita's papa. "You will see what I have for your birthday."

He got out of bed. He took down a package—a big package. He put it on the bed and said, "There, now see what you have."

Pepita looked in the package. It was a new doll. The doll was so pretty!

Pepita took the doll, thanked Papa, and ran to her mama.

Papa smiled and said, "It is good. Pepita does not think about that tree." He went back to sleep.

But Pepita did think about her tree. "Mama will give me my orange tree," Pepita said.

Pepita was singing as she ran to Mama.

"A birthday, a birthday, I have a birthday!"

"Oh, my Pepita," said Mama. "See what I have for you." She showed Pepita a pretty little dress.

Pepita looked at it. It was so pretty, but it was **no** orange tree.

Birthday Packages

"Someone will give me an orange tree at my birthday party," said Pepita. But no one heard her say it when she ran out to play.

Mama smiled as she saw Pepita. "It is good," she said. "Pepita does not think about the orange tree."

Pepita did think about it all morning. She helped her mama get ready for the party. All Pepita's family were to come to the party. All of them knew about the orange tree she wanted.

Mama helped Pepita put on her new dress for the party. Then all her family came. Each one who came to the party had a package.

Pepita looked at each package to see if she could find the one that was her orange tree. She could not tell. Then she looked in each package.

There were dolls. There were books. There were big balls and little balls. There were many other things. There was **no** orange tree.

Pepita didn't say anything, but she didn't know why there was no tree.

"Oh," Pepita said so that no one heard her, "I know who is going to give me my orange tree! One of my friends will do it—Pedro or Anna or one of the others."

So she thanked her family for the packages. Soon she ran out of the house and down the little street.

Her family said to each other, "It is good. Little Pepita does not think about the orange tree."

Pepita went singing down the street.

"A birthday, a birthday, I have a birthday!"

Pedro heard her. Anna heard her.
Her other friends heard her. They all
came out to give her something
for her birthday. Each friend had
something pretty for Pepita.
In one package there was a little cake
with PEPITA on it.

When Pepita went on down the street,
they said, "It is good. Little Pepita
does not think about the orange tree."

But Pepita did think about it.

Pepita came to where the street went
down to the sea. By that time,
she was not singing. She was walking
very slowly. She was doing her best
not to cry.

Now she knew there was
no orange tree for her. She had packages
from all her family and friends—
all but Manolo. She knew he had
no money for an orange tree.

Pepita was very quiet as she walked
down the street to the sea.

149

Manolo saw Pepita and ran to her. "Pepita, Pepita," he said, "did you plant your orange tree?"

"No one gave me an orange tree," said Pepita. "No one at all.
They gave me many things—pretty things, but no one gave me my orange tree."

"You will have other birthdays," said Manolo.

"Here," said Manolo. He gave Pepita a little brown shell. It was a shell like many on the sand.

"The shell is to put something in," said Manolo. Then he said, "My donkey and I will take you for a ride."

Manolo helped Pepita get up on the donkey. They walked on the sand by the sea. On other days Pepita may have laughed. She liked to ride the donkey, but now she was very quiet. She was about to cry.

"Pepita is crying, and on her birthday," Manolo said to himself. "It must not be. It must not be."

Then he knew what he could do. He helped Pepita get down from the donkey's back. "Stay here. I will be back soon," he told Pepita.

He ran down the sand and
over to some orange trees. He saw
an orange under one of the trees.
It was old and not very good.
"That will do," he said to himself.

He took a seed from the orange and
ran back to Pepita.

"For you," he said as he gave her
the seed. He smiled.

Pepita just looked at the seed.
She didn't know what to do with it.
"For me? An orange seed?" she asked.

"An orange **tree,**" said Manolo.

"**An orange tree!**" said Pepita. "Yes, an orange tree for me!" She put the little seed in the little brown shell.

Then she said, "Hurry, we will take the seed to Papa. He will help us plant it." Before Manolo could help her, she got up on the donkey's back again.

Soon they came to Pepita's house. Her family was looking for her. "Pepita, Pepita," they called. "Where are you, Pepita?"

Then they all saw her. "Pepita, Pepita, where were you?" they asked.

Pepita showed them the little brown shell with the seed in it. "Look Mama! Look Papa! Look, all of you," she said. "Look what Manolo gave me. An orange tree! My own orange tree!"

All of Pepita's family looked at the seed in the little brown shell.

Papa looked at Pepita. Then he looked at Manolo.

"You are a good boy, Manolo," he said. "You are so little. But you knew that when Pepita said she wanted an orange tree, she wanted...."

"An orange tree," said Manolo. "So I gave her one."

Papa laughed. "You did. You did," he said. "Now Pepita will plant it. Come, all of you. Pepita will plant her orange tree."

They all came—Mama and all the family.

Papa showed Pepita and Manolo where to plant the seed in the yard. Manolo got the yard ready. Then Pepita put the seed down and put some earth over it.

"My orange tree! My very own orange tree," said Pepita.

Sky Net

I know a busy fisherman
who fishes where it's dry.

He spreads his net
where nothing's wet,
he spreads it in the sky.

He doesn't care to catch a fish
that likes to swim
and splash and swish,
he only has a spider-wish—
to catch a bug or fly.

Aileen Fisher

Word List for ON WINGS OF WORDS

The words introduced in ON WINGS OF WORDS are listed below. They are of three types:

Developmental (boldface type): Words which the authors anticipate most pupils will not be able to identify independently. They are words that will be used in the development of word-analysis skills, or words that should be taught as wholes because they are unsuited to analysis.

Skills Practice (regular type): Words which many pupils will be able to identify with the word-analysis skills that they have developed by that time, but for which other pupils will require more supervised skills practice.

Assumed *(italics)*: Words which pupils are expected to identify independently with skills that have become well established.

For a complete description of categories, see the Teacher's Annotated Edition and Guide to accompany ON WINGS OF WORDS.

9. late	35.	stream	wife
lunch	36.	58. banks	**money**
Miss	37.	59. towns	**leather**
10. slowly		city	80.
11. taking		sea	81.
12.	38. Joe	60.	82.
13.	store		83.
14.	dimes		84. suits
15. later	39. some	61. Louis	85.
16.	**animals**	62. Freddy	86.
17.	40.	63. splash	87.
18.	41.	**frogs**	
	42.	64.	
	43.	65.	88.
19. pickle	44.	66.	
nickel	45.	67. candy	89.
quiet			90. naval
himself			station
Pedro	46.	68.	91. diving
20.	47.		pictures
21. window		69. Crick	swim
22.		Sam	under-
23.	48. Gus	70. leg	water
24.	island	71.	long
25.	**gull**	72.	
26.	49. river	73.	92.
27.	50. sing	74. cricket	93. shore
	51.	dark	94.
	52.	75.	95.
28. princess	53. fast	76. mouth	
castle	water	rubs	
pretty	54. made	77.	96. been
29. marry	55.		**submarine**
30.			97.
31. would		78.	98. getting
32.	56. its		99.
33. golden	trip		100.
goose	57. ice	79. shoemaker	101. waved
34.	snow	elves	102.

103.	118. sick	elephant	**plant**
104.	box	dance	144. doll
105. **happened**	119. keep	132. **Sooki**	think
106.	120.	skin	145.
107.	121. **I'll**	133.	
	122. **cried**	134. **wrinkles**	146. **party**
108. **riding**	123.	tiger	**family**
Hazel		135.	147.
news-		136. **lion**	148. **Anna**
paper	124.	137. **smiled**	149.
109. **spring**	125.	wish	150. shell
110.	126.	138.	151.
111. cars	127.		152. seed
112. **stopped**	128.	139. **orange**	gave
113.	129.	**Pepita**	153.
114.		140.	154.
115. another		141. **Manolo**	155. yard
	130.	**donkey**	
		142.	
116. **Rosa**		143. Mama	
117.	131. **saggy**	Papa	156.

Assumed Words

9. Tommy-	24.	42.	58. met
On-	25. *well*	43. *dime*	became
Time	26.	44.	farms
painting	27.	45.	59. *goods*
doghouse			town
10. Tommy-			60. trips
Too-	28. *laugh*	46.	*falling*
Late	29. *princess'*	47.	
11.	30. *cow*		
12.	31.		61.
13. *fishing*	32. *way*	48. *gulls*	62. Louis'
14. *sad*	33.	49. *hook*	*bank*
15.	34. *holding*	Gus'	63. *frog*
16. *lunchtime*	35.	*hide*	64.
17.	36. *laughing*	50.	65. *splashes*
18.	37.	51.	66.
		52.	67. *eating*
		53.	
19. Peters	38. Bill's	54.	
Peters'	39. *balls*	55. *set*	68.
named	*toy*	*helped*	
20. Bill	*toys*		
21.	*rabbits*		69. Ted
22. *times*	40. *balloons*	56. *rivers*	*sometimes*
kinds	*whistles*	*same*	*astronauts*
23. Pedro's	41. *owned*	57. *mountains*	*doctors*

70. Sam's
    sleeping
71. Ted's
72.
73. far
74. crickets
75. Crick's
76. sings
    wings
77.

78.

79. shoes
    sell
    pair
80.
81. pairs
82.
83.
84. shoe-
    maker's
85. stayed
86.
87.

88.

89. bay
    Hall
    frogmen

90. maybe
91. tanks
    backs
92. frogman
93. ones
    Peter's
94.
95.

96.
97.
98. sub-
    marines
99.
100.
101. calling
102. wave
103. someday
104.
105.
106.
107. suit
    helping
    splashed

108. hen
109. under
110.
111.
112. hurrying
113.
114.
115. Hazel's
    news-

paper-
man
picture

116. Rosa's
117. animal
    raining
118. coat
119.
120. wing
121.
122.
123.

124.
125.
126. being
127.
128. lots
129.

130.

131. baggy
    kick
    elephants
    danced
    kicked
132. fits
133. fit
134.

135. yours
136. lot
137.
138.

139. singing
    Pepita's
    stores
140.
141. oranges
    hat
142.
143.
144. thanked
145.

146. packages
    someone
147. dolls
148.
149.
150. birthdays
    sand
151. crying
    donkey's
152.
153.
154.
155.

156.

159